Look at You!

Making a Puppet

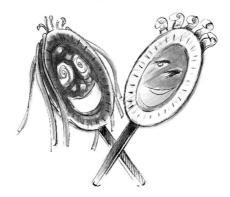

By Margaret Ballinger
and Rachel Griffiths

Illustrated by Meredith Thomas

HOUGHTON MIFFLIN COMPANY

BOSTON

ATLANTA   DALLAS   GENEVA, ILLINOIS   PALO ALTO   PRINCETON

To make a puppet just like you, collect:

paper,   scissors,   crayons,

a paper plate,

glue,

a stick,

and some tape.

Draw a face on the paper plate.

Make some hair by

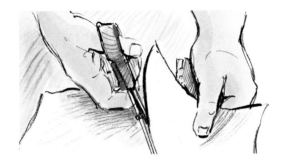

cutting,

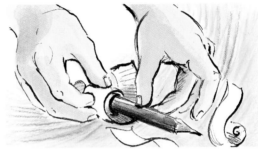

or curling,

or fringing,

or tearing paper.

Glue the hair on the paper plate.

Tape the stick to the back of the paper plate.

Look at you!